Natalie's Newscast
Stay tuned!

James Otis Harris

Illustrations by
Danh Tran Art

Dadielte Production 2022

Moreno Valley, Ca

ISBN- 978-0-9981419-3-0

Published and distributed by
Dadielte Production
P.O. Box 1266
Moreno Valley, CA 92556-1266

First Printing
Cover design by Danh Tran Art

Dedication:

This book is dedicated to my sister Gail who became the first African American female telephone installer in Riverside Ca. Worthy of a Natalie's Newscast.

Introduction

Natalie loves history more than dancing with her friends in 4th grade. Learning about famous people was always exciting. During classes, she would daydream about all the wonderful and interesting individuals in history- If she could speak with them, that would be a dream come true. She believed the only way to truly learn was from the figures themselves.

After school, Natalie would rush home to watch the local newscasters on TV interview famous characters from around the world. Natalie wanted to be a news reporter like the people on TV. She wanted her own newscast in the worst way. But where could she go to find well-known people and facts from the past? Natalie decided to visit parks, statues, museums, libraries, and any other place where important figures and information about history could be found.

She remembered all good newscasters had two things, a microphone and a TV camera. She grabbed a golden microphone from an old karaoke machine and decided to use her cell phone to record. She stuffed them into her purple and mauve backpack with the sliver sparkles- Natalie was ready to go.

She jumped on her bike with Lucy, her yellow Labrador retriever running by her side, and rode as fast as she could to the park. She took out her mic and tied her cell phone to the top of Lucy's head, and pointed it at a statue. To her surprise, the mic started to glow and the red light on her cell phone started blinking. She realized the microphone had come to life. Natalie yelled, "Yippee!" She could have her broadcast. She held her magic microphone which she called Mia.

Mia turned to her with a large grin and said, "3, 2, 1, Natalie, your newscast has begun!"

She held Mia tightly, looked into the camera phone on top of Lucy's head, and said "I'm Natalie, Welcome to station K.N.O.W, you are now in the know wherever you go!"

Whenever Natalie points her magic mic at sculptures, paintings, or anything that has to do

with history, Mia, the microphone comes alive.
These are the episodes of Natalie's newscast.
Everyone Stay tuned!

Natalie's Table of Contents

Aviate to be Great!

Bessie Coleman

Aviate to be Great!

When Natalie entered the museum, she didn't know which area to visit first. She strolled into a large room with a sign that read, "The Wonderful World of Aviation." Hanging from the ceiling were planes of all different sizes and styles. She saw replicas of the Wright Brothers' plane, the Hindenburg blimp, a rocket ship and hundreds of other vintage and current aircrafts.

Looking around, she spotted a picture of a young African American women pilot wearing a flight cap with goggles. A brown scarf hung from her neck. She looked dashing and familiar at the same time.

Natalie thought this young lady resembled her friend, Ashley who wanted to be a pilot when she grew up. That's all Ashley talked about.

Natalie wanted to hear her story and thought, "This is a good time for my newscast, this interview will be fun.

Natalie placed her cell phone on Lucy's head. Positioned her in front of the picture while holding Mia, her magic microphone up to the frame. The microphone started to glow. Mia said, "3,2,1 Natalie your newscast has begun."

The picture was of Bessie Coleman who turned and smiled at Natalie.

Bessie said with a grin, "I'm happy you came by. I feel the need to fly! Did you come to interview me? I have a lot to say, you'll see."

Natalie stepped closer to the picture and said, "Yes I did. My friend Ashley, heard you were the first African American female pilot in America. Is that true? Because you're not in any of my history books, trust me, I looked. Me and my viewers would like to know how you became a world-famous pilot?"

Bessie adjusted her flight cap and said, "Sure Natalie, I may be a mystery but I'm a part of America's great history.

I wanted to fly, but because of my gender and color, I wasn't given a chance. So, I taught myself French, and in 1909 moved to France. I refused to hear the answer no, therefore I packed my bags, I was determined to go.

I went to a flight school that was color blind. They taught me to fly, what a find! My instructors were great and oh so kind."

Natalie became really interested in her story. She asked, "Can you tell the audience, where and when did you fly while in France. The viewers want to hear more."

Bessie was now leaning out from the picture frame and continued, "I flew high and low, morning noon and night. From the evening dusk to the early light.

I soared in the sky from hour to hour, I even flew around the Eiffel tower. The clouds were my floor which allowed me to soar. Flying for me was like an open door.

On June 15th 1921, I received my international pilot's license, my journey had begun. I became the first African American female aviator, I was ready to roar. It didn't matter if I was rich or poor, becoming a pilot was in my core. Who could ask for anything more."

Natalie lifted the mic closer to Bessie and asked the question, "Did you ever get home sick? What were your plans when you came back into the USA to stay?"

"Yes," said Bessie. "There were times I felt alone. I missed my family and wanted to come home.

I came back to America with my license in hand. I wanted to fly, do stunt shows and open a flight school, I had a plan."

Natalie put her arms out like she was flying around the room and said, "What type of flying did you do?"

Bessie laughed, "I became a stunt pilot and a traveling barnstormer. I became quite a performer. I was dubbed Queen Bess because I was more not less."

Natalie turned back and saw Lucy's head tilting to one side. "Lucy," she said. "Sit up straight." Lucy's tail began to wag.

"I have another question," Natalie asked. "So, you became famous in the United States and it didn't matter your gender or race?"

Sitting back in the picture, Bessie said,

"That's right! Because of my story an elementary school, a street at O'Hare Airport and a stamp were named after me. I was even inducted into the Aviation Hall of Fame. If I had to do it over, I would do everything the same.

Natalie, I want everyone listening to follow their dreams, no matter how far away they seem. Also, tell Ashley one day she will be a pilot like me, never give up, that's the key."

Natalie couldn't wait to tell Ashley what Bessie said. Natalie stepped closer to the picture and said, "I have one last thing I want to say. Bessie, your inspiration is second to none, because of your passion America won. Thank you, Bessie, I mean Queen Bess."

Bessie laughed again. "Thank you, Natalie. Come again soon! I will be waiting for you in this room."

Natalie wished she could stay longer but it was getting late. Besides, it was time to feed Lucy. Natalie thought to herself, 'Learning about Bessie was cool, something I didn't learn in school. I will share her story as much as I can, I just became a Bessie Coleman fan.'

Before leaving, Natalie turned towards Lucy, smiled at the camera and said, "This is Natalie at Station K.N.O.W. You are now in the know wherever you go. See you next time on Natalie's Newscast- stay tuned."

No Small Feat!

Robert Smalls

No Small Feat!

Natalie noticed a poster nailed to a telephone pole. The sign read, "Come see the famous ships now showing at the local harbor. Hear about legendary admiral's, sailors and seamen of the United States Navy.

Natalie decided to see what well-known ships were anchored on the waterfront. She jumped on her scooter and rode it to the marina. When she arrived, she saw a remake of a famous Civil War Cargo ship called The Planter. In front of the transport ship was a large bronze bust of an African American man wearing a straw hat. The name plate was inscribed, Robert Smalls, American Hero. The plaque read, *He was a slave who stole a* vessel from the Confederate army, sailed it to freedom and became a U.S Congressman.

Natalie knew a great story when she read one. But she wanted to hear it from him. It was time for Natalie's Newscast. While removing her cell phone from her backpack she realized Lucy was walking towards the hot dog stand licking her lips.

She grinned and said, "Lucy, as soon as the interview's over, we'll get a hot dog just for you, but for now, sit still."

Lucy nodded her head yes and sat in front of the bust. Natalie adjusted the cell phone on Lucy's head. "There you go."

Natalie finished taking Mia the Magic Microphone out of her backpack and held Mia up to Mr. Small's. The golden microphone started to glow when Mia said, "3,2,1 Natalie your newscast has begun."

The shiny bronze bust shouted, "Ships' Ahoy! Natalie."

"Hello Mr. Smalls." Natalie said. "Welcome to my newscast. This is Station K.N.O.W. I just read you're an American hero. Can you tell my audience how you became celebrated for stealing a ship?"

"Sure, it all started while I was enslaved. I wanted my freedom, I wanted to be brave. For days, months and years, I studied my Captain's traits. For my plot to succeed, I needed to wait. Therefore, I learned to sail the Captain's boat, I knew this was my only hope.

"On that fateful morning of May 13, 1862, I knew exactly what to do. Take the Planter and sail it to be free. But I had to do it without being seen. Therefore, I put on the Captain's hat, wore his coat, acted like him while navigating his boat. I took my family and a few others along for the ride; they had to be quiet and of course, hide. We were headed for a better life; the promise of liberty was nice.

"I used the hand signals that I was taught. I prayed we wouldn't be caught. Moving beyond the first check point was a good sign, of what was in front of us and what we left behind. The American flag flew in the distance; our freedom would be determined in an instant. We passed the last checkpoint; I knew we were safe. Our next stop, a brand-new place.

"We delivered the ship to the Union forces, and told them where we'd been. This vessel was our gift to President Lincoln.

"Because of my exploits, I became an overnight sensation; I was applauded around the nation; The abduction of the ship triggered weeks of celebration; my next stop was a good education."

The aroma from the hot dog stand caused Lucy to turn her head again. "Just a few more minutes, Lucy," Natalie said. "This is important stuff. Mr. Smalls, what you did was amazing is there more?"

Mr. Smalls took a deep breath and spoke.

"Natalie that was the beginning, but not the end. I helped over 5,000 African Americans enlist in the Union Army and fight in the Civil War. Each one knew what we were fighting for. I did as much as I could for myself, my family and the common good.

"I fought and won many union battles. Because of my bravery, I was never rattled.

"I was rewarded by becoming the first African American captain in the U.S Navy. Where I came from, the very thought was crazy."

"Wow!! According to the plaque you also served in the South Carolina U.S House of Representatives for 12 years. That's a long time, is that true"

"Yes, in 1874 I was elected to Congress and re-elected numerous times; I was one of a kind.

"When I was a free man, I purchased my former master's house. Something not heard of in the South".

Natalie couldn't believe this was the first time she'd heard the story of Mr. Smalls.

"Is there anything else you would like to share with our viewers before we go?"

"Absolutely, in 2007, the vessel USS Smalls was named on my behalf. This was a great honor from my past.

" I believe my story needs to be told of how my crew and I were brave, courageous and bold.

"Natalie, I hope my story made you proud. Sometimes I think about what I did and say Wow!! I was an advocate for freedom and spoke out loud. I want to thank you for the interview. This is something I always wanted to do."

"Mr. Smalls, what you accomplished was really neat, you helped America that's no small feat." Natalie giggled, "No small feat."

She turned back to Lucy and said, "Until next time, this has been Natalie's Newscast, reporting from the Ship and Boat Show. This is Station K.N.O.W you are now in the know, wherever you go-stayed tuned!

You Can Bank on It!

Maggie L. Walker

MAGGIE LENA WALKER

You Can Bank on It!

Natalie was visiting Richmond, Virginia when she saw Lucy barking at a statue in the middle of town. Her two front paws rested on the base; A pigeon sat on its shoulder.

Towering over Natalie was a tall figure of a woman walking with a check book in hand. Natalie said, "I wonder who she is?"

Lucy knew what to do. She grabbed Natalie's backpack and laid it at the foot of the sculpture.

'My viewers would love to hear her story.' Natalie thought.

When Mia, the microphone was placed next to the statute, Mia said, "3,2,1 Natalie, your newscast has begun."

The sculpture was of Maggie L. Walker who exclaimed, "Hello Natalie, would you like to learn how to deposit, withdraw or get credit. I can show you how to do it."

"Hello," said Natalie. "I'm from Station K.N.O.W. My audience would like to know why is there a statue of you carrying a checkbook. Can you explain?"

Lucy was looking up trying to get a full body shot of Mrs. Walker.

"Let's see where to start. My story began in 1899. I worked for the Independent Order of St. Luke at the time. It was right after the Civil War. This was my first real job, but not a chore. The organization provided mutual aid and insurance to members in need. The Order of St Luke planted a seed.

"I rose to the ranks of Right Worthy Council's secretary, where my duties varied. I learned to run a financial institution. One day this would be a solution.

"However, the organization was on the verge of bankruptcy with less than $31.00 to our name. To lose the organization would be a shame.

"When the chief leader stepped down, I stepped up. The financial district I was going to disrupt. It was my time to change the game, nothing would be the same. We were in debt, but everyone knew I was a safe bet."

"What did you do next?"

"In 1901, I laid out a step-by-step plan. I wanted a bank, a department store and a newspaper under one brand. Economic independence was my stand. We stressed the principles of pride, thriftiness and cooperation. It was the corner stone of community relation."

Natalie looked at Lucy and said "Are you getting all this." Lucy nodded. "Please continue, Mrs. Walker."

"On November 2nd 1903, I became president of The St Luke Penny and Saving Bank. I didn't do it by myself, I have many to thank. It opened in the capital of the Confederacy during Jim Crow, not a place you wanted to go."

"What! You owned a bank!" She couldn't believe her ears. "Not only were you the first African American women, but the first woman in America to own and be president of a bank. Is that right?"

Maggie gave her two thumbs up. "By 1920, our influence had grown. My bank helped customers purchase over 600 homes.

"In 1924, the bank ballooned to one hundred thousand members; it didn't matter your race or gender. We now had one-half million dollars in reserve. We gave the community what they deserved."

"That sound great! Did you have a catch phrase for your bank?"

"Of course, *Let us make a bank that will take the nickels and turn them into dollars. If we could do that, we would stand taller.*

"Sadly, because of the market crash in 1929, our funds and membership began to decline. We merged with other black owned banks to survive; this kept my dream alive. We became the newly formed Consolidated Bank and Trust. We came together in unity, a must. Our bank remained the largest continuous black-owned bank into the 21st century. This was a great victory."

"Mrs. Walker, the 19th amendment gave women the right to vote. Were you part of that movement?" Natalie asked.

"Indeed, after it passed in 1919, my efforts for equality picked up steam. I organized a women's registration drive. It was a good time to be alive."

Natalie looked down at the display which listed her many accomplishments. It read:

Maggie L. Walker- self-made millionaire, civil rights activist, entrepreneur, first female bank president. She led a bank, a store, a newspaper, organized a boycott against a street car company and started the first African American Girl Scouts in the South.

Natalie was amazed, she said, "Mrs. Walker you were famous. Did you have famous friends too?"

Mrs. Walker laughed, "Booker T. Washington, W.E.B Dubois and Mary McCloud Bethune were some that dropped in. They were more like family than friends."

A crowd began to gather. Natalie nodded at Lucy. "We have to wrap it up. Others may want to discover Mrs. Walker's extraordinary life, and my camera battery is running low.

"One last thing, according to the sign, your statue was unveiled on July 15, 2017. What was that like?"

Mrs. Walker looked out over the city. "I was thrilled!" she said. "Hundreds of people were there, it showed they cared. Come visit my house. It was turned into the Maggie L. Walker Historical landmark, a great place to start."

"Not only was this educational, but it was inspirational. You're more than a balance sheet, you're someone everyone should meet," said Natalie.

Feeling a little tired, she crossed her legs and leaned against Maggie. "This is Natalie, reporting live from the Maggie L. Walker monument in Richmond, Virginia. This has been Station K.N.O.W. You are now in the know, wherever you go-stay tuned!"

I Was Taylor Made

Major Taylor

RIDE-A-LONG

BIKE SHOP

Major Taylor

I Was Taylor Made

Natalie was waiting for her mountain bike to be repaired at the Ride-a-Long Bicycle Shop. The owner suggested she look around while he patched her tire. There were new and shiny cycles hanging along the walls of the store.

There was a large poster pinned to the wall of a young African American man in a cycling uniform. He stood behind a vintage racing bike. The poster looked like it was from the 1900 hundreds.

Natalie whistled to Lucy for her backpack. "He looks like a champion," she said. "Let's see what he has to say. We have some time before we can ride anyway."

She turned on the camera and Mia the magic mic said, "3,2,1 Natalie your newscast has begun" Lucy barked, "Ruff."

"Hi! I'm Natalie from Station K.N.O.W. We have a question. Why is there a poster of you hanging in the bike shop? Are you famous or something?"

The poster became animated, "Major Taylor is my name. Cycling is my game. My real name is Marshal Walter Taylor, but let me explain my claim to fame.

"I lived in Indianapolis, Indiana as a child. I was one of eight-What a crowd! My father worked for a family that purchased a bike. It was given to me as a gift, it changed my life. I rode and practiced every day; I just couldn't stay away.

"When I was 12, I landed my first job in a bicycle store. Who could ask for anything more?

"I conducted bike tricks for kicks and to drive in business, I wore a soldier's uniform when I performed. They called me Major which became the norm. Cycling became my call. I give it my all."

Natalie liked doing cycling tricks too. She asked, "Did you ever race?

"Definitely, my boss entered me into my first contest in 1892. It was a 10-mile race, he didn't believe I would place. He said, after a mile I could stop. He just wanted to advertise his shop. I was nervous, scared and couldn't move. But there was something I had to prove. That afternoon, he learned a lesson. Not only did I win, but I won by a whole 10 seconds."

"You sound like you were fast," Natalie said as she sat on a tandem built for two.

"Under my own power, I could go 40 miles per hour," Major explained.

"For years I competed in amateur contests; determined to be the best. I dominated and was not overrated. You should have seen their faces when they witnessed a young African American winning; this was just the beginning.

In 1895, I entered in a 75 mile sprint. I was told I would be harmed if I rode. However, at the end I knew I was safe; I was the only one to finish the race."

Natalie noticed that Lucy had stopped filming. Her paw was tangled in a bike spoke. "Lucy!" she said as she helped free him. "Stay out of trouble!" Turning back to Mr. Taylor, she asked, "Were you ever a professional cyclist?"

"Yes, as an amateur I was the best, turning pro was next. I was born to ride, tailor made and ready to get paid.

"I became professional in 1896 at Madison Square Garden. I won in front of 5,000 guests, but there was no time to rest. That qualified me for the famous Six Day Race. To win you would need endurance and pace. I dropped out after 1,700 plus laps and came in eighth. But that showed I was great."

"Major is a good nickname, but did you have others?"

"Sure, in 1897 during a Pro Tour, the press started calling me, "The Worcester Whirlwind," "The Black Cyclone" or "The Ebony Flyer." My reputation was on the rise and went higher.

"Between 1898-99, I held seven world records at one time. My one-mile record from a standing start stood for 28 years. This brought my competitors to tears.

"In the same year, I won the World Cycling Championship in Canada-the first African American in the world to do so, I was ready to go. I had the title and no rival."

"How many times did you win?"

Mr. Taylor looked up thinking and said, "I won 47 out of 52 competitions. I was in great condition. I became the first African American celebrity athlete. I was the one to beat."

It sounds like you broke world records every time you raced."

"I did. In 1900 at Madison Square Garden, I went head-to-head against a champion in front of 6000 fans. I won and there was cheering from the stands.

"I retired in 1910, it was time to let someone else win. During 1930, I wrote my autobiography titled, *The Fastest Bicyclist in the World*. It was one of a kind at its time."

Natalie saw out the corner of her eye, her tire was just about repaired. "Mr. Taylor, Any parting words before we go?" She asked.

"Sure! To your viewers I want to say, I was a pioneer. I had to blaze my own trail. If you do that you won't fail."

Natalie thanked Mr. Major Taylor for his interview. As she hopped on her bike, she said, "Until next time, this is Natalie from K.N.O.W, live from the Ride-a-Long Cycling Shop. You are now in the know, wherever you go. Stay tuned!"

Mail Call!

6 Triple 8

The 6 Triple 8

Robert Smith
dated 1945.
from Mr. and Mrs. Smith.

U.S. Pos

"However, we did experience loss and difficult times because of our gender and race. But we confronted it with style and grace.

"Unfortunately, three of our soldiers died in a jeep accident. They were heaven sent. They're the only women honored and buried in the famous Normandy memorial park, that day was dark. Some of our soldiers are resting in the legendary Arlington Cemetery in Washington D.C. The appropriate place be."

Natalie noticed a slogan on the poster which said, "No Mail, Low Morale."

"What's that?" Natalie asked.

"That's our battle cry. We completed our mission and that's no lie."

There was only a few more people in line before it was her turn at the counter. Natalie wondered, "Did you receive any awards for your service or participate in events?"

"Absolutely, we marched in fabulous French parades. On November 30, 2018 a monument was erected in Fort Leavenworth, Kansas and dedicated to us. For our service I trust. Also, the Army approved a meritorious award for the 6 Triple 8. There are bills in Congress for the Congressional Gold Medal -that would be great."

"I didn't know anything about the 6 Triple 8. I'm going to tell all my friends, I can't wait."

It was Natalie's turn to mail her letter and waved good-by to the major.

Natalie turned and said, "This has been station K.N.O.W. "I'm live with Major Charity Adams from the 6 Triple 8. You are now in the know wherever you go. -Stay tuned!

Paul's Grand Plans

Paul Revere Williams

Paul's Grand Plans

Vacationing in Hollywood, California was going to be a blast. The family visited famous landmarks like the Hollywood sign, Grauman's Chinese theater, and even strolled on the Santa Monica pier. The day was going great until her parent suggested they explore some illustrious homes and buildings in the Los Angeles area.

Natalie said to Lucy, "I didn't come all this way to see buildings. We have houses at home-Yuk!

During their drive, Natalie saw prestigious neighborhoods, exquisitely designed buildings and beautifully landscaped residences. They stopped at one particularly stunning structure for sale and noticed a sign on the property which read: Architecture by Paul Revere Williams.

"Have you heard of him?" Natalie asked her father,

"Of course, he's the famous African American architect, born right here in Los Angeles."

Natalie didn't know any architects, let alone any African American ones. She had to hear his story.

With Mia in hand, she held her up to the home. Mia said, "3,2,1, Natalie your newscast has begun."

The structure declared, "From the floors to the ceilings, you should know who designed these unique homes and buildings. Paul Williams was known as the architect to the stars. His designs raised the bar."

"That's awesome! Architect to the stars how did that happen?"

"As a child, he drew everything he could find and wanted to design. Paul lost his parents at four, but grew up wanting to be an architect and more. There were no African American architects at the time. It was a tall hill to climb."

Looking puzzled, "Did people try to stop him from his dreams?"

"Sure did! In high school his teacher once told him he would never become an architect because in her words, 'Your own people can't afford you, and white people won't work with you. So, for a living what will you do?' But to his dreams he held true, and went to school. He became the first African American architect west of the Mississippi and graduated from USC. When he opened his own practice L.A. it was the place to be."

Natale noticed Lucy sniffing around, "What celebrities did he know? I haven't heard about him at the movies."

"Actually, over six decades from the 1920's to the 1970's, he designed homes for Frank Sinatra, Lon Chaney, Desi Arnaz and Lucille Ball- that's not all! just to name a few to give you a clue. To this day, numerous celebrities have owned his homes. They are held in high esteem. Owning a Paul Williams home was everyone's dream."

"Was it hard for him to find work as an African American architect in Los Angeles?"

"Unfortunately, yes. Since whites felt uncomfortable working side by side, a method he had to devise. Paul's clients sat across from him, and he learned to draw and sketch upside down- as funny as it sounds. He wanted to place them at ease, he wanted their business and to please. He became famous for that skill. Every project was a thrill."

"Were homes his only projects?"

"Heavens no! He was part of a team that designed the famous theme building at the Los Angeles International Airport, the iconic open dome, where L.A. flights call home. He also designed the L.A. Courthouse and Public Housing for the city. He gave to the little and many. Moreover/, he envisioned the AME and Founders' Church-Those were just perks."

"Ok, but what about hotels? We're staying at this really elegant placed called the Beverly Hill Hotel."

"Funny you should ask-the Beverly Hills Hotel is one of the most recognized iconic buildings you'll find in Los Angeles. Did you know, the front for the Beverly Hills sign was his creation? That was so exciting, because the words are in his own handwriting."

"His buildings look cool, but how can I tell if he designed a home?"

"Because of the graceful, long, curved staircases and marvelous ceilings that were shaped like domes inside his homes. They're always mentioned, It's a hallmark of his magnificent intentions."

"I bet he lived in one of those fantastic homes."

"Unfortunately, no, because of the racial restriction on African Americans at the time. He was unable to purchase a home in Caucasian neighborhoods which wasn't good."

"My viewers want to know, is there anything else he developed?"

"He designed St. Jude Hospital for his friend, Danny Thomas, free of charge. He had a dream and designed it in the shape of a star."

Looking for some place to take a nap, Lucy stopped filming. "We have to be going anyway. My dad wants to see the L.A Coliseum. Mr. Williams didn't design that too, did he?"

"No, but he designed his own dwelling.

"So, he was the first African American architect west of the Mississippi in 1923, first to receive a fellowship from the American Institute of Architects in 1957, and the first African American to receive a gold medal in architecture from the University of Southern California in 2017. "

"Wow!! Anything else?"

"Since you're asking, he designed the Nevada Museum of Art and the Long Beach Naval Station which is no longer there and hundreds of others around the country- each one rare. With over 3,000 designs; each one a find."

Natalie woke Lucy and with the Hollywood sign in the background Natalie said, "Someday, I want my own Paul Williams home. But for now! This is Natalie, reporting live from the historic Paul R. Williams building in Hollywood, California. You are now in the know where ever you go-stay tuned!"

Traveling Men!

Pullman Porters

Traveling Men

This was the first time Natalie and Lucy walked through the Old Train Station in Union City. Walking past a display case, she noticed a vintage model train with African American figurines who wore white coats and blue hats. Some were helping passengers with their bags; some were serving food and others were taking tickets.

The sign above the display case read, *The Brotherhood of The Sleeping Car Porters. Learn how The Famous Pullman Porters changed America.*

Natalie's train was scheduled to leave in two hours so she had time for an interview. She stood on a stool to get a better look. Natalie took Mia from Lucy's mouth. "3,2,1, Natalie, your newscast has begun! " it said.

The porter taking the tickets looked up and said, "Are you ready to take a ride on the luxurious Pullman Train?"

Natalie responded, "Sure, where are we going?"

"We're going miles with smiles," the porter said,

"Your sign says 'Famous Pullman Porters.' I haven't heard of you before? What makes you famous?"

The Porter tipped his hat, smiled and said, "In 1865 after the Civil War, employment for African Americans was bleak and poor.

"The only job's available were working in fields or on trains. To receive a steady paycheck, wearing a uniform was a gain. The opulent Pullman locomotive was magnificent and money well spent. The Porters were kind, gracious, courteous and recognized for our service."

"Mr. Porter," Natalie said, "I bet you traveled a lot."

He removed his hat, "Indeed, we sometimes traveled seven days a week. Most times we didn't eat or sleep. We were on call 24 hours a day; the extra time was not in our pay. Sometime there was harsh discipline, but we still had to smile and grin.

"A better life we sought, even though we were away from our families a lot. We shined shoes, served food, waited on passengers and more, even when the conditions were poor. Our routes went from the North to the South. We were traveling men no doubt!

"We did our jobs with dignity and grace. We knew it would further our race."

"Mr. Porter, my mother told me to tip whenever I get service on the train. Is that ok?"

Mr. Porter remembered the days when he received tips. He said, "Because our pay was low, we were thankful for the gratuity more than you know.

"However, as the years went on, our circumstances became worst. We could no longer hold our tongues; we were ready to burst.

"We demanded a solution; so, we came together and created a union, a team, to protect us against bad policies and schemes."

Lucy started to get a little nervous hearing trains pulling into the station.

"Don't worry, Lucy," Natalie said. "Trains are fun! Mr. Porter tell my viewers about this new union."

"Absolutely. In 1925, there was a union membership drive. A. Phillip Randolph was the elected leader, and was called Chief. With him aboard it was a relief. Ashley Trotter and Milton Webster came on as well. They had some stories to tell.

"They formed the Brotherhood of Sleeping Car Porters. Their representation covered from border to border. This would be the first African American Union in the United States. Our pay, health, living conditions were at stake. We had to win at all cost, or everything would be lost.

"After 12 long years, in 1937 we won. That was our prize, we could no longer be denied. The decision restored our integrity and pride. We had the wind at our backs and a glide in our stride."

"So you defeated one of the largest companies in America?"

"That's right! It was time to take our rightful place with honor, integrity and respect. We wouldn't accept anything less."

"Were there other famous porters my viewers should know?"

"Sure, here are some fruits from our tree, a branch of our great legacy. Thurgood Marshal, Matthew Henson, Malcom X and Wilma Rudolph to name a few. Natalie you should check, you may be a descendant too."

"I sure will, Mr. Porter," She said. "I want to thank you for your time. My train is arriving soon. Is there anything you want my audience to remember?"

"Of course, our kids and future generations became engineers, academics, doctors, business leaders and teachers" Mr. Porter said, "they became esteemed community and world leaders. Everyone became a Pullman Porter believer."

Natalie's train arrived right on time. She tugged on Lucy's collar. "Time to go! However, until next time, this is Natalie from K.N.O.W, live from the Union Train Station with the Famous Pullman Porters. You are now in the know, wherever you go-stay tuned."

Nanna's Green Gem

Negro Motorist Green Book

in town after sundown. We slept on the side of highways many of times, traveling-while- black was a grind.

"The book was kept up to date, whether here or in another state.

"Our slogan was: "Carry your Green Book with you, you may need it." Good advice to follow, it never rang hollow."

"That sounds like a handbook to have while on the road back then."

"Yes, it was used as the black person's "Triple A" if you were traveling, on vacation, or just on your way.

"It was great and published in all 50 states. There were other places you might want go. It was used in the Caribbean and Mexico."

Lucy wagged her tail causing dust from the floor to cover Natalie. "Oh great Lucy, thanks a lot!" she said, as she wiped dust off the camera lens. "Mr. Green, how long did you print the book? Where could you find them? How many did you sell?"

She had so many questions.

Mr. Green caused the pages to turn. He said, "We printed the Book from 1936 to 1966. There was a problem I wanted to fix.

"You could find them lying around or in an Esso Gas station from town to town. We sold over 2 million copies a year. This relieved a lot of anxiety and fear."

Natalie heard Grandma Dee walking downstairs. She knew she would be calling soon.

Mr. Green continued, "Did you know in 1964, the Civil Rights Act ended legal segregation? This law helped the entire nation. After that, there was no need to print another addition. The book had completed its mission.

"To some this book is a mystery, but it's an important part of history. It's Nanna's green treasure, without measure.

Natalie was thrilled. She turned to Lucy and said, "I was wrong, not only did I find something good, I learned about a gem of history that's been missing."

Mr. Green said, as he closed the book. "Thank you for your time, you've been so kind. Come back and take another look. This chest contains other great books."

"I will," Natalie said.

Before closing the chest, she promised she would tell her friends about the great legacy of *The Negro Motorist Green Book* and how it changed travel in America for African Americans.

Natalie saw Lucy covered with dust from head to tail. She laughed. "We both need a bath."

She removed dust from her face and stated, "Once again, this is Natalie live from Station K.N.O.W reporting from my nanna's attic. Now you know, wherever you go-stay tuned!"

Yippie! General Order No.3

Juneteenth

Yippie! General Order No.3

Natalie and her family were finally ready to attend the annual Juneteenth Day Celebration. Everyone in the car was excited. This was Natalie's first time; she didn't understand the celebration or all the fuss. But she thought,

'Well, a festival is a festival. Let's have some fun. Anyways with Lucy by my side, I'll have someone to talk to.'

As they entered the fairgrounds, she was handed a piece of paper. Printed on top was the title, "General Order Number 3."

Natalie thought, 'What's this? I'm here to have fun not read.' Just as she was about to throw the paper away something caught her eye. It read in bold letters:

All slaves are free. This involves absolute equality.

Natalie could smell a great interview coming. She asked her mother for her backpack and said she wanted to take Lucy for a walk. Her mother said, "OK, but stay close."

Natalie retrieved Mia, her magic microphone from her bag and positioned Lucy over the parchment when Mia said, "3,2,1 Natalie, your newscast has begun!"

The scroll lit up and said, "You know me! I'm a copy of Executive General Order Number 3!"

Natalie felt bad when she said, "Actually I don't.... sorry."

The document said, "I thought it was clear why you're here. It's about the celebration we have every year. Stay awhile, let me bend your ear."

Pointing her nose into the air "Ok," Natalie said as she laughed. "But only for a little while. I smell some bar-b-que with my name on it."

The Order responded, "Sure thing! this is how the story unfolds of how the enslaved in Texas were never told about a Proclamation that changed this nation.

"You see, President Lincoln signed the Emancipation Proclamation in 1863. This meant people living in bondage were free. However, the fighting continued for two years more. You may have heard of it; the Civil War. The Union Army defeated the Confederate Soldiers in 1865. There were cheers and even high fives.

"Slowly, one by one, each Southern state gave up the institution. They believed their way of life was ruined. The state of Texas was the last holdout. I'm sure they had their reasons, no doubt."

Natalie thought, "Humm, Do you know why Texas didn't tell everyone they were free?"

"Natalie, it's like this, Texas was resistant because they wanted free labor. They vowed not to tell anyone, friends or neighbors. Texas especially didn't inform the enslaved. Because if they knew, questions would be raised, and freedom craved."

Natalie's mouth fell wide open. "Wow!" she said, "So who told them?"

"On June 19th, 1865 General Gordon Granger along with some 2,000 Union troops marched into

Galveston Bay, Texas and announced the declaration that more than 250,000 African Americans were freed by executive decree. They were shocked, happy and in disbelief that chattel slavery was abolished under their feet."

Natalie glanced at Lucy and then back at the Order. "Juneteenth, That's a funny name. Why is it called that?"

The Order laughed, "It's a blend of two words June and nineteen, together it's really keen. The celebration is called by many names, Jubilee, Emancipation Day, Freedom Day, and Black Independence Day. Anyone you use is ok. The first observance commemorated was on June 19th 1866 one year to the day. It was a tribute they wanted to pay. The great state of Texas formally recognized the holiday in 1938. It was a long time coming but never too late."

Natalie could smell corndogs cooking. She asked, "What are some events that go on?"

The Order exclaimed, we have rodeos and street fairs where goods are sold, re-enactments, cookouts, family reunions, singing where our stories are told. You may hear famous African American writers reading that day. There's so much to do you'll want to stay. You could even be Miss Juneteenth and awarded a crown. There's tons to do, how does that sound?"

"General Order Number 3, I get it now! I have one last question for my viewers. I now understand why it's important to us, but why should anyone else care about Juneteenth?"

"Good question, Natalie, because when the order was received everyone in the country was finally free. It was time for our nation to live up to its constitutional decrees, of life, liberty and justice for all. This is what the Emancipation Proclamation saw.

"In 2021, it was formerly recognized as a federal holiday. It was time for remembrance, unity and a day off with pay. Natalie, not to brag, but Juneteenth has its own flag. It's red, white and blue with a big white star in the middle to give you a clue. This cannot ever be understated, remembering those who were liberated."

Natalie said, "I have a greater appreciation for Juneteenth and what's it's about. It's much more than a holiday."

Lucy started wandering off towards the bar-b-que stand. Her mother would be coming soon. It was time to wrap up the interview. "Thank you,

General Order Number 3." she said. "There's no place I would rather be."

She ran after Lucy with Mia in her hand and said in a rushed voice.

"This is Natalie, reporting live from the annual Juneteenth Celebration. This has been station K.N.O.W. You are now in the know where ever you go-Stay tuned!"

James is the author and creator of his children's book Natalie's Newscast. His love of history guided him to discovery and highlight extraordinary African American's whose contributions have gone unnoticed. By using her gifted imagination Natalie's Newscast is a blast where she interviews people from the past.

James resides in Southern California. He hopes the stories in Natalie's Newscast bring you and your child as much joy as he experiences writing them.

Made in the USA
Monee, IL
31 January 2023

25713453R10048